Publisher: Daoudi Publishing
ISBN: 978-1-960809-09-4
Author: Rita Ortega

SOLAR ECLIPSE

GUIDE AND ACTIVITY
BOOK FOR KIDS

By Rita Ortega

Introduction

Welcome, young explorers! Are you prepared to take a journey of discovery into the fascinating world of solar eclipses? We're going discover today the fascinating science behind these amazing events, and why they are so captivating!

What is a solar Eclipse? It's a little like playing hide-and seek between the Sun and Moon. The Moon can cover the Sun and cast a shadow on Earth. We call this a solar eclipse. Why does this happen, though? The Moon's orbital path and its position in relation to the Sun and Earth are responsible for this. A solar eclipse happens when everything aligns perfectly. Like a huge cosmic puzzle, everything comes together.

Imagine the sky becoming darkened during the daytime, birds singing less and the temperature falling. A solar eclipse is exactly what you'll see! It's like the day suddenly turning to night.

This book will teach you a great deal about solar eclipses. From understanding the model for the solar system, to learning the different types, this book is a must-read. Solar and Lunar Eclipse Charts are included, as well as easy-to follow instructions on how to safely observe a solar eclipse. Have questions? Even those difficult, unclear questions will be answered. The adventure does not end there! There are many exciting activities to choose from, including Word Search Puzzles to challenge your mind and Engaging Solar Eclipse Coloring for your creativity.

Are you ready to explore the fascinating world of solar eclipses? Explore the science, beauty and history of these amazing moments with us!

Let's begin our journey and discover the beauty of these cosmic marvels together!

Eclipse Adventure

One day, in the blue skies above, something truly magical happened: a solar eclipse.

Imagine the Sun to be a giant, glowing light ball that brings warmth and daylight. Like our own super-star! Now, the Moon. Well, it's kind of like a cool and shiny rock who loves to dance on our planet. The Moon likes to play peekaboo with the Sun every now and then. The Moon covers the Sun, which causes the sky to dim for a while. This is a solar event! A solar eclipse is like the Moon hugging the Sun in a cosmic embrace. The Sun's bright ring peeks out behind the Moon and creates a ring. This is what we call a special "annular" eclipse.

Some times the Moon plays hide-and seek even better, and completely covers the Sun, making it all dark. It's called a total eclipse. Like the Moon telling us, "Today I am going to completely cover the Sun!"

Remember this: Even when the Sun is hiding, it can still be very bright. This can harm our eyes. Use special glasses to view this stunning show.

These are amazing sky moments that we don't see very often. They show us how beautiful and mysterious the world can be. If you hear about solar eclipses, you'll be able to tell that it's actually the Sun, Moon, and Earth playing a magic game of hide and seek in the heavens!

hello

Total Solar Eclipse

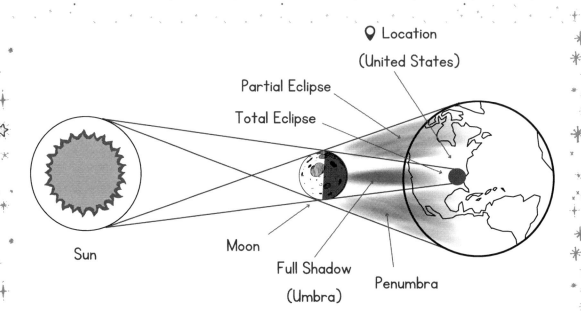

Location (United States)

Partial Eclipse

Total Eclipse

Sun

Moon

Full Shadow (Umbra)

Penumbra

Solar Eclipse Words Made Simple

- Moon: Earth's natural satellite, a round object that orbits our planet. Partial Eclipse: When the moon covers part of the sun, creating a crescent shape in the sky.
- Total Eclipse: A special moment when the moon completely hides the sun, turning day into night.
- Full Shadow (Umbra): The darkest part of the moon's shadow, casting complete darkness during a total eclipse.
- Penumbra: A lighter part of the moon's shadow, creating a partial eclipse with reduced sunlight but not total darkness.
- Location of solar eclipse: The specific place where a total eclipse can be seen, with the moon fully covering the sun, making it dark.

Phases of Solar Eclipse

The planets that come together in the sky   Moon   Sun

1.The solar eclipse is just starting!

The sun is alone, and the moon's special show hasn't begun yet.

The edge of the Moon starts to overlap the edge of the sun. and Now the magical eclipse begins!

The moon almost hides the whole sun, and that's when a total eclipse begins!

Now, during a total solar eclipse, the sun is completely covered by the moon.

2. The solar eclipse is finishing up!

The total solar eclipse is still happening, and the moon still covers the sun.

The moon begins to move away, and parts of the sun's circle start to show again.

The moon starts to move away from the sun.

The sun is back to normal, the eclipse is over.

Types of Eclipses

The difference between solar and lunar eclipses

Solar Eclipses:

A solar eclipse is a little like playing hide-and seek with the Sun and Moon. Imagine the Sun shining brightly in the sky. Imagine the Moon as a huge ball who loves to play hide and seek with Sun.

The Moon is in front, as if it were a lamp, during a solar eclipse. This happens when the Moon covers up the Sun. For a brief period, it is dark even during the day. Like the Moon saying "I found You, Sun!" The "solar corona" is a ring, or circle, of light that surrounds the Moon.

Lunar Eclipses:

Another fun game is the lunar eclipse. The Earth, Moon, and Sun all play together this time. The Earth is right in the middle. The Earth is like the shadow that you make when you hold a torch up to a wall.

A lunar eclipse occurs when the Earth's shadow covers the Moon. The Moon might appear reddish and a bit dark, just like a delicious strawberry!

What gets covered is the major difference between both eclipses. In a lunar eclipse, the Moon temporarily hides the Sun, making the day dark. In a solar eclipse, the Earth's shadow turns the Moon into a different color, making it look like a strawberry!

The solar eclipse and the lunar eclipse are both amazing natural shows that remind us just how exciting and wonderful our universe can be. If you watch the sky carefully, you may see one of these fun eclipse games.

Types of Eclipses

Solar Eclipse

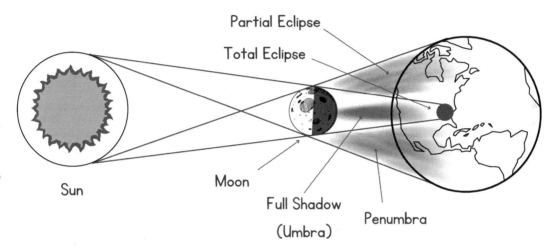

Partial Eclipse

Total Eclipse

Sun

Moon

Full Shadow
(Umbra)

Penumbra

Lunar Eclipse

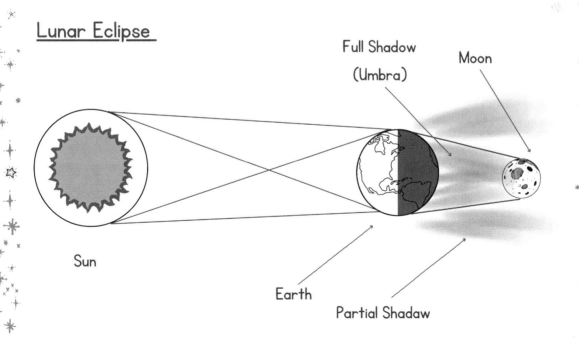

Full Shadow
(Umbra)

Moon

Sun

Earth

Partial Shadaw

Total Solar Eclipse of 2024

<u>Date:</u> The magical moment is April 8- 20- 24.

<u>Place:</u> The 2024 total eclipse of the sun will be visible throughout North America. If you live anywhere in the United States, but especially in Texas, Arkansas, Ohio and Maine, this is a rare treat. People in the United States will see the Moon covering the Sun entirely for a short time, turning it into night. This is like the Sun having a little nap at the middle of the afternoon.

The experience of this eclipse will be unforgettable for everyone, and especially for kids. Do not look directly into the Sun when an eclipse is occurring without wearing proper protective eyewear. If you want to see these celestial wonders safely, use special eclipse glasses or pinhole projectors.

It's like nature is revealing secrets to us. Eclipses teach us our universe has many wonders. It doesn't matter if it is the "rings" of fire in the annular or total eclipses of 2023 and 2024. They are both amazing. So let's learn and have fun with these wonderful eclipse experiences.

Eclipse Map

2023 Annular Solar Eclipse

2024 Total Solar Eclipse

Solar Eclipse Instructions

Safety is always the first priority! Use your solar eclipse glasses, or watch the show online or on TV. This is a fun and safe way to enjoy a magical solar eclipse without damaging the eyes. Enjoy your show, but be careful!

Unsafe Ways to View the Eclipse

- It is important to know the things you should not do during an eclipse.
- Always wear eye protection when you are in the sun. Direct sunlight can damage your vision and cause permanent damage.
- Avoid wearing regular sunglasses. Regular sunglasses do not provide adequate protection for your eyes.

How to safely enjoy a Solar Eclipse

- Solar eclipse glasses can protect your vision. They contain special filters. Always wear them before gazing at the sunlight.
- Online or on TV? You can view solar eclipses via some websites and television channels.

Safe and Unsafe Tools

Safe tools:

Solar Eclipse Glasses: These glasses are designed to protect your eyes during the eclipse.

Unsafe tools:

Regular Sunglasses, Phone, Camera: These won't protect your eyes and are not safe for eclipse viewing.

Solar Eclipse Telescope or Monocular: These tools can be unsafe for kids without proper adult supervision and knowledge. It's better to stick with eclipse glasses.

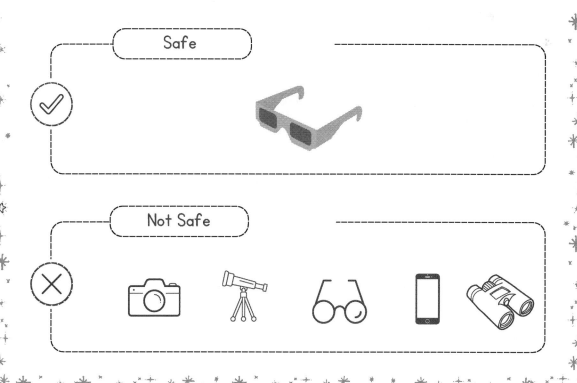

hello

Fun Solar Eclipse Facts

- During a solar eclipse, animals behave differently because they mistakenly believe that it is now nighttime.
- Other planets such as Mars and Jupiter also have solar eclipses.
- The Great American Eclipse of 2017 has been one of the most-watched eclipses ever.
- One of the earliest solar eclipses recorded in history was in China, in 2134 BCE.
- Some people in the past believed that during an eclipse, a big dragon or a giant frog tried to eat the Sun. Ancient Chinese believed that solar eclipses were caused by a giant dragon eating the Sun.
- The word "eclipse" comes from "ekleipsis", a Greek term that means "abandonment," "darkening of a celestial bodies,"
- In 1919, Albert Einstein's theory of relativity was confirmed through a solar-eclipse experiment.
- Eclipses can be rare, and a location may not experience one for many years.
- Astronauts aboard the International Space Station have a unique opportunity to observe eclipses.
- Hubble, and other telescopes in space can observe eclipses.
- The interval between two total solar eclipses at the same place can be as long as hundreds of year.
- Many people attend eclipse parties in order to view this spectacular celestial phenomenon.
- Scientists can forecast solar eclipses months in advance. It is possible to plan to view an eclipse in the future.
- Due to the distance between the Earth and the sun, they appear nearly the same in size. That is why the eclipse can be so perfect.
- Some people like to collect souvenirs of the eclipse, such as coins or stamps. They keep these items in their homes to remind them of that experience.

Write Notes

held

Questions and Answers

1. Why does the Moon cover our Sun?

- A result of the Moon's position in the sky, it covers the Sun. Sometimes they are perfectly aligned.

2. What happens during a total solar eclipse?

- Looks like the Sun is darkened by a huge bite. Outside, it gets a bit darker.

3. Can we view a solar Eclipse?

- You shouldn't look at the eclipse without special eyewear. It could hurt your eyes. Use special eclipse glasses only.

4. Why does the Sun disappear in an eclipse?

- The Moon's shadow is what makes the Sun vanish. It's as if the Moon and the Sun are playing hide-and – seek.

5. What is a solar eclipse?

- The Moon appears reddish when the Earth passes between the Sun and Moon.

6. Why does a red moon appear during a solar eclipse?

- The Moon changes colour because Earth's atmospheric conditions bend the light from the Sun and cause it to change color. On the Moon, it's almost like a unique sunset.

7. Can we view a Lunar Eclipse?

- You can safely watch lunar eclipses. It's not necessary to wear special glasses, as the Moon only changes colors.

8. Why do we not have eclipses everyday?

- The Earth, Moon, Sun, and other factors have to be aligned correctly for an eclipse to occur. It's almost like solving a puzzle.

9. Are there eclipses on other planets?

- Yes, there are other planets that can experience eclipses. These planets have similar moons and stars, but their eclipses work differently.

Questions and Answers

1. How often do solar Eclipses occur?

- Every 18 months, solar eclipses can be seen in different places on Earth.

2. What is a solar eclipse total?

- The Moon can completely cover the Sun and cause it to be dark for a very short period of time.

3. Can the Sun & Moon play hide & seek?

- Sun and Moon never play hide-andseek. It's almost a special occasion when they do.

4. Why does a partial solar eclipse only last a short while?

- Solar eclipses tend to be brief because the Moon crosses the sky quickly, covering the Sun only for a couple of minutes.

5. How do we see a distant solar eclipse?

- To see a solar eclipse, you may have to go to a distant location. They are viewed by people around the globe using telescopes and cameras.

6. How do you know when an eclipse will occur?

- Scientists do have the ability to predict when eclipses occur. They use computers and other special tools to work it out.

7. What do people do during a solar eclipse?

- Some people choose to watch solar eclipses through special glasses or TV. Others gather together to celebrate the exciting event.

8. Can there be a simultaneous lunar eclipse and a solar one?

- The lunar eclipse is at night while the Moon is still up. And the solar eclipse is during the sun's day. They don't occur at the very same time.

9. What's the longest solar eclipse ever?

- The longest total solar eclipse could last 7 minutes. And the longest total lunar eclipse, 1 hour 47 minutes. They are short, spectacular shows.

Word Search

L	D	L	Y	Q	X	K	W	S	E
U	G	I	M	O	O	N	P	H	L
L	E	G	C	R	E	X	Z	A	U
Y	X	H	A	T	C	K	J	D	D
S	D	T	F	H	L	V	E	O	T
B	A	N	S	S	I	D	S	W	O
T	R	G	O	U	P	I	K	P	T
G	K	L	L	N	S	I	Y	J	A
E	F	C	A	W	E	A	A	F	L
K	V	C	R	S	L	U	N	A	R

Eclipse	Light	Total	Sun
Lunar	Moon	Shadow	Dark
Solar	Sky		

Word Search

B	M	K	A	P	G	U	U	S	M
G	O	W	S	A	Q	N	U	T	B
O	O	O	T	R	O	I	M	A	G
V	N	S	R	T	L	V	B	R	L
I	L	V	O	I	J	E	R	S	A
S	I	L	N	A	X	R	A	J	S
I	G	M	O	L	K	S	A	G	S
B	H	M	M	Y	K	E	O	P	E
L	T	A	Y	E	A	R	T	H	S
E	V	P	D	P	Y	R	M	G	C

Astronomy	Universe	Glasses	Map
Partial	Visible	Earth	Umbra
Moonlight	Stars		

My Scribble

My Scribble

Thank you

Thank you very much for picking up a copy of my book. You could have chosen from a variety of different books, but you decided to take a chance and go with this one. So, thank you for purchasing this book and reading it to the conclusion.

Before you leave, I'd like to request a tiny favor from you. Could you please consider leaving an Amazon review? The greatest and simplest way to promote independent authors like me is to write a review. Your input will assist me in continuing to write the types of books that will assist you in achieving the results you desire. It would mean a lot to me if you could let me know your opinion. Your feedback is valuable and will help shape the future of my work. Your support means the world to me, and I'm truly grateful for your trust in my book. I hope it has provided you with valuable insights and an enjoyable reading experience. Your decision to explore the world of solar eclipses with me is greatly appreciated.

As we journey through the pages of this book, I hope you've found it informative and engaging. Your curiosity and love for learning inspire me to keep creating educational and captivating content. Thank you for being a part of this exciting adventure, and I look forward to your thoughts and feedback.

Once again, thank you for choosing my book, and I hope it has enriched your understanding of the fascinating world of solar eclipses.

Made in United States
Troutdale, OR
03/16/2024